Hello...

Written and illustrated by Bridget Campbell, photography by Jo Tennant,
designed by Craig McIntyre, with afterword by Lauren Eliott Lockhart.

I have a sister Trudy,

She looks a lot like me.

I think she's fantastic,

Come meet her and you'll see.

She has the biggest smile

Of anyone I know,

When she's happy and excited

She really lets it show!

It's not all smiles and laughter

Some things make her frown.

Sometimes she feels grumpy

Sometimes sad and down.

There's usually a reason
That makes her feel that way,
So I switch on my hero mode
And chase those blues away.

Some say Trudy's different
And maybe that is true.
She's got an extra chromosome
What's that to me and you?

There's nothing wrong with different

We're all different in our way,

With different likes and dislikes

And different ways to play.

Trudy loves to play and mess around
The muddier the better.

On the beach when I get wet
Trudy gets even wetter!

At the park she loves the swings

I push her really high.

She laughs and giggles, claps her hands

And soars into the sky.

Trudy just loves music

She's thrilled to sit and sway.

When I help her stand up tall

She's dancing all the way.

Trudy loves to play and mess around
The muddier the better.

She hasn't started walking

She'll get there in the end.

She's a supertastic shuffler

And you should see her bend.

Though Trudy doesn't talk yet
She has lots of things to say.
We're all talking with our hands
In a very clever way.

So, if you meet someone "different"
And don't know what to say,
Why not smile and sign hello
And make a friend that day.

Afterword by
Lauren Eliott Lockhart

The girl and boy you see in this book
are our son and daughter, Patrick (four)
and Trudy (two). When Trudy was born with
Down's Syndrome, my husband Alex and
I wanted to find a book we could share with
her brother that was simple and positive,
but didn't raise too many questions.
Nevertheless, children are curious
creatures and it isn't always easy
to find the right explanation.

Bridget Campbell wrote and illustrated this poem, which presents a typical sibling relationship and sends a clear message about accepting and welcoming difference. We decided to use Jo Tennant's photos of Patrick and Trudy to give an insight into the realities of their relationship, and to show first-hand the kinds of things that they enjoy doing together.

We hope this book provides a good starting point for conversations about diversity and difference. We have included some more information about Down's Syndrome and a list of websites which we hope you will find useful.

Our overall message is one of acceptance, and who better to share this message than a child aged four, for whom Trudy is just his little sister? Patrick and Trudy have a lovely relationship and look after each other in different ways. Patrick helps her to stand and uses simple words and signs to help her understand. In turn, Trudy comforts Patrick when he's upset and she is a frequent ray of sunshine in our house.

We hope Trudy's smile brightens your day when reading this book. And if you happen to meet a boy or girl like Trudy, you might say or sign 'hello', if they don't say 'hello' to you first!

Hello

Through the eyes of a child

Here are a few questions our family has been asked about Trudy by children we know and some we don't. We hope our answers can support parents to tackle some of those tricky questions without dampening children's curiosity:

Can I catch it? (Izzy, 10)

No, you can't catch it. It's not like chicken pox. Trudy was born with Down's Syndrome and it won't ever go away.

Will she get better? (Reece, 8)

She isn't ill. It is part of what makes her who she is, like your brown hair or your freckles.

Does it hurt? (Bronwyn, 9)

No. Down's Syndrome does not cause her pain.

When did she get it? (Harry, 9)

Trudy has always had Down's Syndrome.

Why don't I have Down's Syndrome? (Patrick, 4)

Nobody knows why some people are born with Down's Syndrome and some aren't. Down's Syndrome means that Trudy will find things more difficult than you, so she will need your help.

She looks like my sister Florence? (Max, 4)

Florence has Down's Syndrome like Trudy and that means their faces look quite similar, but Florence is more like you than Trudy.

Why isn't she talking yet? (Unknown, 7)

It will take Trudy longer to talk because she needs help to learn. Speaking slowly or using signs helps Trudy to communicate.

Why is she on her bottom? (Unknown, 8)

Trudy is still learning to walk and she finds it much easier to move on her bottom at the moment. She will learn to walk eventually.

She's small, isn't she? (Unknown, 11)

Children with Down's Syndrome grow at a slower rate than other people, so they are often smaller. They even have their own growth chart!

More about Down's Syndrome

Down's Syndrome or Down Syndrome was named after Dr John Langdon Down in 1886 who first described the condition. There are three types of Down's Syndrome but most people have Trisomy 21, which means they have an extra copy of the 21st chromosome in their bodies. Chromosomes typically come in pairs and carry the information in our bodies to make us what we are. The other types of Down's Syndrome are Translocation and Mosaic.

Although people with Down's Syndrome have similar facial characteristics, they resemble their families more than they resemble other people with Down's Syndrome. As you will see in the photos, Patrick and Trudy look very much alike. People often say that children with Down's Syndrome are always happy. We know first-hand that isn't always the case! They experience a range of emotions, just like the rest of us.

The extra chromosome can mean a lot of different things for different people, but it generally means that children with Down's Syndrome need more time to learn to do things like walk and talk. This is because they all have physical characteristics that affect their development in different ways, and they will all have a learning disability to differing degrees. Other children have to learn to be patient, and give them the time and space to figure things out for themselves.

As children with Down's Syndrome may take longer to talk and walk, they often have a physiotherapist or a speech and language therapist who works with them. These professionals provide invaluable support to children and families, as well as nurseries and schools, by teaching them signing systems to support their language development, or exercises to support their physical development. There are several signing systems in the UK, but the most important thing to remember is that signing offers visual support for a child with Down's Syndrome and slows down the speaker by making them choose key words more carefully. Clear and simple language is very important when speaking to someone with Down's Syndrome. Signing also helps children with Down's Syndrome communicate their own needs and feel included despite possibly having speech and language difficulties or delays.

This early support lays the foundations for many more opportunities for people with Down's Syndrome in schools, further education and in the workplace, so that they can lead full and rewarding lives as active members of their community. There are also organisations and charities that support people with Down's Syndrome and their families, and we would like to acknowledge their support. Without them, we wouldn't be where we are today.

About the author

Bridget Campbell has always loved reading and drawing. Studying English Literature at university gave her a glorious four years of sitting in comfy armchairs, disappearing between the pages of books to get a sense of the world from different perspectives.

Working for a learning disability charity before and after university resulted in Bridget pursuing a career in health care. After qualifying as an Occupational Therapist, Bridget worked for the NHS for 10 years in mental health and learning disability. Meeting Patrick and Trudy inspired Bridget to create this picture book to share their story and unique, joyful perspective on the world.

Photograph © Isabel Lohss-O'Sullivan

Where's bunny?

Trudy LOVES her
soft, cuddly bunny.

Do you have a favourite toy?
How many bunnies are
there in the story?

Turn to **page 36** for
the answer!

Community connections

The idea for 'Trudy & Me' began with a conversation between Bridget and Lauren in their local play park, but the book wouldn't have come to fruition but for the encouragement, enthusiasm and skills of a great many more people in our local community. Two in particular deserve specific mention:

Craig McIntyre

Hailing from Joppa, Portobello, Craig is a graphic designer who loves to communicate concepts and bring projects to life. This is achieved professionally, but also at a local level through meaningful conversations and the desire to share back and help elevate ideas, working with like-minded individuals, using their passion to help their community and surroundings.

Jo Tennant

Jo Tennant is an award-winning photographer with a passion for capturing the joy of the everyday. Bringing this philosophy to 'Trudy & Me', Jo has captured Trudy and Patrick's special sibling connection and exuberance for life.

Jo lives in Portobello with her family and has founded **20 Photos**. Find out more about Jo's work here: jotennant.com

Find out more

Down's Syndrome Scotland
dsscotland.org.uk

Down's Syndrome Association
downs-syndrome.org.uk

Down Syndrome Cork, Ireland
fieldofdreamscork.ie

Mencap
mencap.org.uk

Positive About Down Syndrome
positiveaboutdownsyndrome.co.uk

Wouldn't Change a Thing
wouldntchangeathing.org

Makaton: language programme
that uses symbols, signs and
speech to enable people to
communicate.
makaton.org

Lamh: manual sign system
used by children and adults
with intellectual disabilities and
communication needs in Ireland.
lamh.org

Language Creates Reality:
cards exploring the use of
language when talking about
Down's Syndrome.
languagecreatesreality.com

The Yard: Scottish charity
supporting disabled children
and young people (aged 0–25),
and their families, through
adventure play.
theyardscotland.org.uk

Enable: Scottish campaigning,
advice and advocacy charity
for people with additional
support needs.
enable.org.uk

Enquire: Scottish advice service
for additional support for learning.
enquire.org.uk

Blogs

Trudy and Patrick
Lauren Eliott Lockhart's blog
trudyandpatrick.com

Downs Side Up
downssideup.com

Don't Be Sorry
dontbesorry.info

Book website

Follow our journey:
trudyandme.co.uk

To my family...

BC for Al, Lachlan and Matilda for being incredible and always believing this book would get finished!

Answer:
Trudy doesn't have her bunny on **page 6** and this might be why she is upset. But Patrick is running to the rescue, holding bunny on the next page. Phew!! There are **14** bunnies in the book, plus one more if you count the picture of a bunny on **page 23**.

First published in 2022 by Bridget Campbell
trudyandme.co.uk

Text and illustrations copyright © Bridget Campbell 2022

The moral rights of Bridget Campbell to be identified as the author of this work have been asserted in accordance with Copyright, Designs and Patents Act 1988

British Library Cataloguing-in-Publication Data

A catalogue record for this book is available from the British Library

Designed by Craig McIntyre
Printed and bound by Kingsbury Press